# DOT·TO·DOT
## in Color

# NATURAL WORLD

# DOT·TO·DOT
## in Color

# NATURAL
# WORLD

**30** challenging designs to improve your mental agility

SHANE MADDEN

## METRO BOOKS
New York

**METRO BOOKS**
New York

An Imprint of Sterling Publishing Co., Inc.
1166 Avenue of the Americas
New York, NY 10036

ISBN 978-1-4351-6443-7

For information about custom editions, special sales, and premium and
corporate purchases, please contact Sterling Special Sales at 800-805-5489
or specialsales@sterlingpublishing.com.

2 4 6 8 10 9 7 5 3 1

www.sterlingpublishing.com

Credits
Publisher: Kerry Enzor
Managing Editor: Julia Shone
Senior Editor: Philippa Wilkinson
Editorial Assistant: Emma Harverson
Designer: Mike Lebihan
Production Manager: Zarni Win

Printed in China by RR Donnelley

MIX
Paper from
responsible sources
FSC® C101537

# Contents

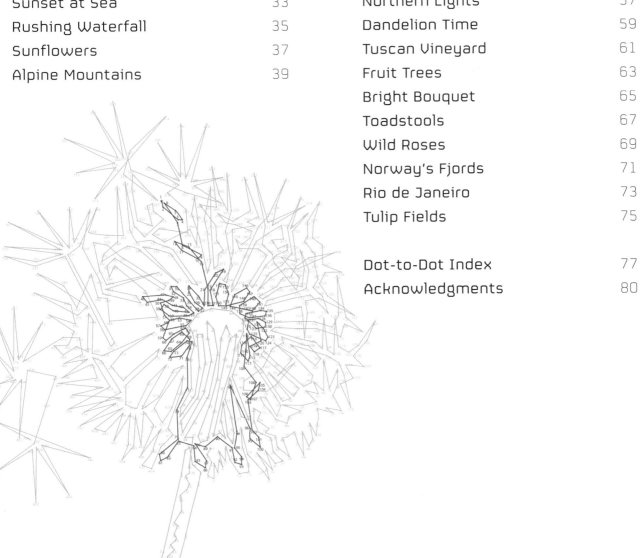

# Introducing Dot-to-Dot in Color

Get ready to dive into a world of color with the 30 vivid designs in this collection. Each of the dot-to-dot puzzles in this book has been inspired by the natural world's riot of color, from the burning golds of a sunset to the jungle canopy's verdant greens and the neon dance of the Northern Lights. Simply unravel the web of numbered points to reveal a stunning artwork. You'll be wowed every time.

## Bringing Color into Your Day

Dot-to-dot puzzles are a great way to switch off from the distractions and stresses of our 24/7 world. Taking the time to concentrate on an absorbing task can help us achieve a state that positive psychology identifies as "flow." Flow activities enable us to tune out from our day-to-day concerns and become immersed with energized focus on the task we are completing. This taps into a central tenet of mindfulness, that is to say being fully involved in the present moment.

More than this, flow activities are characterized by positive channeling of attention and energy. Completing a challenging task gives us a mental boost and encourages a more positive, go-getting attitude. We can use flow activities to revitalize and refresh our minds, and gear ourselves toward a more proactive mind-set.

Use the 30 puzzles in this collection to set you up with a successful approach for the day, or wind-down with them in the evening. The dot-to-dots can be tackled in sections, or completed in a single sitting—simply fit them into your day to discover a sense of achievement and a calmer, more focused mind.

## Join the Dots

Each of the puzzles in this book has over 400 numbered points to untangle. Once you get started, you will find the rhythm, following one point to the next to reveal a dynamic scene from the natural world. Before you get started, turn to page 10 for top tips on how to approach these extreme dot-to-dots.

Choose which puzzle to start with by turning to the Dot-to-Dot Index on pages 77–79. A thumbnail of each image will help you take your pick from vibrant tulip fields, majestic fjords, and cascading waterfalls. Scenes from throughout the natural world are rendered in full spectrum and are perfect subjects for this eye-catching dot-to-dot treatment. All of the pages are blank on the reverse side, which means you can remove and frame your work when you're done.

# How to Use
# This Book

Before you dive into the colorful world of the dot-to-dots in this collection, read through the following pages for advice on how to use this book and for top tips on completing these fiendish puzzles.

A key for each puzzle shows the order in which the color-coded sections should be completed. Follow this order to ensure no premature crossing out of numbers or dots in other sections. The key also lists how many numbered points there are in each section so you can easily identify when you have completed that color. Read the color order down each column, starting with the left column.

Each colored section starts with number "1." The first point is indicated by a star to identify the beginning for each line.

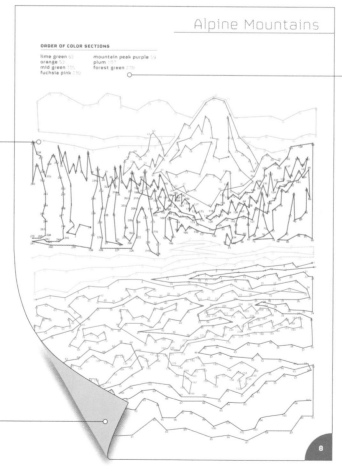

Alpine Mountains

**ORDER OF COLOR SECTIONS**

| | |
|---|---|
| lime green | mountain peak purple |
| orange | plum |
| mid green | forest green |
| fuchsia pink | |

Match your colors to those listed in the key for each section. You have the freedom within each color to decide your own tones or shades should you wish.

The reverse of each page has been left blank so that you can remove your finished puzzle and display if you wish. However, some reverse pages have color keys. Check the back of each design before removing as you may need the key to complete the next puzzle in the book.

Turn to pages 77–79 to find finished thumbnails for each of the puzzles in this book. You can use this index to help select which scene from the natural world you would like to try next, or if you need some guidance to complete the puzzle.

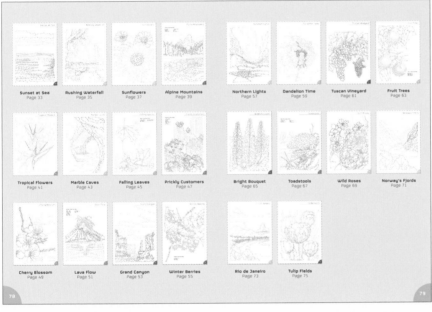

## CHOOSING YOUR TOOLS

*To complete the puzzles accurately, it is best to use a fine-nibbed felt-tip or roller ball pen in each of the colors listed in the key. You need to be able to keep your lines sharp and clear in those areas where the dots are close together.*

*The colors listed in the key provide a palette guideline. You have the freedom within each color to decide your own tones or shades. Whatever you choose, the finished result will be a highly colored scene from majestic mountain ranges, peaceful woodland glades, or sun-soaked orchards. You may wish to take some time testing your chosen pens on a spare sheet of paper before starting the puzzle.*

# Tackling the Dot-to-Dots

The illustrations in this book have been designed with vivid color palettes to evoke the hues of the natural world. The colored sections are generally worked from lightest color to darkest. Follow the order listed in the key, working down each column, to ensure the best result.

Each colored section starts with number "1" and progresses chronologically to the end dot. The total number of dots in each section is listed in the key so you can identify when you have completed each section. It makes sense to join all of the dots in one section before progressing to the next, following the order recommended in the key.

Everyone will have their own method for approaching these fiendish puzzles, but below are some tips to help you get started.

1. **Prepare your tools:** We recommend using fine-nibbed pens (see Choosing Your Tools, page 9) to complete the dot-to-dots, but you can also use colored pencils. If choosing pencils, make sure that they are sharp before you begin so you can keep your lines fine in detailed areas.

2. **Get comfortable:** You can choose to complete these puzzles wherever you like—on your commute, on a lunch break, in a café. However, to get the most out of the puzzles it is best to choose a quiet spot where you will not be disturbed so that you can fully focus on the task in hand. Having a flat surface to work on with plenty of space may also help.

3. **Use a ruler:** Some of the points are quite far away from each other, and using a ruler will help to keep your lines sharp in more congested areas.

4. **Take it in order:** Each puzzle has been designed to be completed in a certain color order as denoted by the accompanying key. Follow this order so as to avoid crossing through any numbers before you need to use them.

5. **Don't worry:** Try not to get frustrated if you go wrong. Simply locate the error and go back to the last correct point. You will still have a beautifully colored puzzle when you finish.

6. **Closer look:** In some detailed areas you may wish to use a magnifying glass to help you read the numbers clearly.

7. **Pen bleed:** Each reverse side of the puzzle has been left blank so that you can remove your designs once completed, and also to protect against ink bleeding through the page to obscure the following design. If you are concerned about your pens bleeding through the paper, simply place an 8 x 12 inch sheet of blank paper behind the puzzle that you are working on.

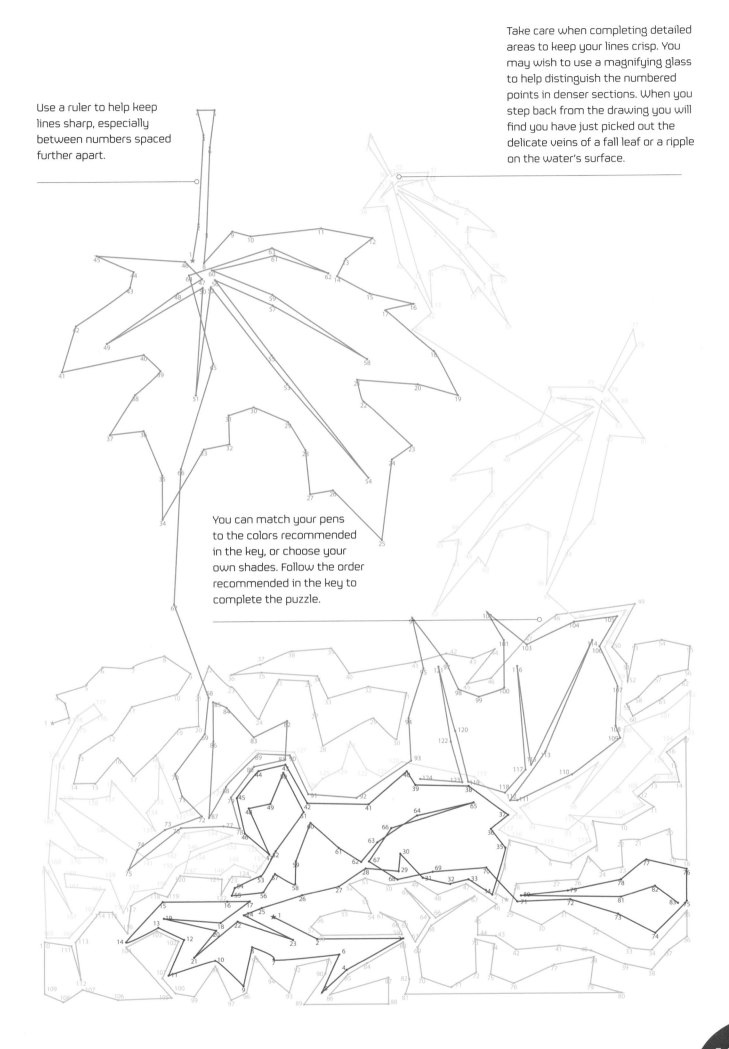

Use a ruler to help keep lines sharp, especially between numbers spaced further apart.

Take care when completing detailed areas to keep your lines crisp. You may wish to use a magnifying glass to help distinguish the numbered points in denser sections. When you step back from the drawing you will find you have just picked out the delicate veins of a fall leaf or a ripple on the water's surface.

You can match your pens to the colors recommended in the key, or choose your own shades. Follow the order recommended in the key to complete the puzzle.

# Creating with Color

Using color has been made easy in this book, with expert color-coded palettes developed for each image to bring the scene strikingly to life—and you can bring your own flair to each drawing by coloring in the completed puzzle.

## Coloring Tools

While you need a sharp pencil or fine-nibbed pen to keep your lines crisp when completing the dot-to-dot puzzle, you can choose from a range of options to add color to your image.

**Colored pencils** are the tool of choice for most coloring in as they can be used to create subtle tonal variations within the image as well as adding fine details. Another option is **watercolor pencils**, which can create a lovely painterly effect; and for a bolder approach, **felt-tip pens** create rich, vibrant images with strong color. You can also experiment with **pastels**, **paints**, and **crayons** to realize a range of different styles. Have fun and explore the different artistic effects you create simply by changing your coloring tools!

## Basic Shading Techniques

There are a number of different shading techniques that you can use to add color to your dot-to-dot design, all of which create slightly different effects.

### Hatching
Hatching is a series of lines drawn together to give a sense of filled color. The hatching lines can be either straight or curved, and can be drawn close together to give a smooth effect or further apart for a more sketchy look. Hatching is a great way to add color quickly to an image.

### Crosshatching
In crosshatching one set of lines overlaps another set. Like hatching, crosshatching can be drawn with the lines close together to create a solid effect or more spaced out with white spaces remaining. For areas of color that you want to appear very smooth, close crosshatching is the best method.

### Circular shading
You can also shade with small circles rather than straight lines. Again, you can create denser or more roughly colored areas depending on how close together you keep your lines. This method can be useful for creating texture within your image.

Drawing hatching lines close to and overlapping one another creates a smooth area of color.

When drawn further apart from one another the hatching lines remain distinct.

Crosshatching when lines are drawn very close together can create a dense solid color.

Spaced further apart, crosshatching lines remain distinct and show areas of white space.

## Adding Light and Shade

Create shape and bring depth to each design by adding areas of light and shade. Shading with colored pencils or watercolor pencils is the easiest way to do this. The simplest method is pressure shading, where you place more or less pressure on your pencil to achieve a darker or lighter shade. Alternatively, shade the full area with the lightest shade then go back over areas that you want to make darker, adding extra layers of color to achieve the desired effect.

Shading with pencils can leave flecks of white and show lines between more heavily and less shaded areas. To smooth out the color in your image you can use a colorless blender pencil. Available from most good craft stores, blender pencils can be applied over the top of colored pencils to better merge the different tones.

To intensify shading, you can layer darker colors over basic shading. Layering colors in this way will create a different shade from either of the original colors used and can make for an interesting tonal variation. You can also use different tones within a color range to achieve more depth in your image.

## Creating Shape

When adding light and shade to create shape in your image there are three key terms to remember: highlights, shadows, and mid-tones. To create a sense of perspective you will want to add highlights to areas of the image that would be in the sun and shadow in those areas that would be facing away from the light source—mid-tones are those areas in between. You can use the shading techniques above to create these areas of light and shade within your dot-to-dot design.

# THE
# DOT-TO-DOT
# PUZZLES

# Down in the Jungle

**ORDER OF COLOR SECTIONS**

golden yellow 169
lime green 404
orange 223
light leaf green 80
mid leaf green 123

# Pine Cones

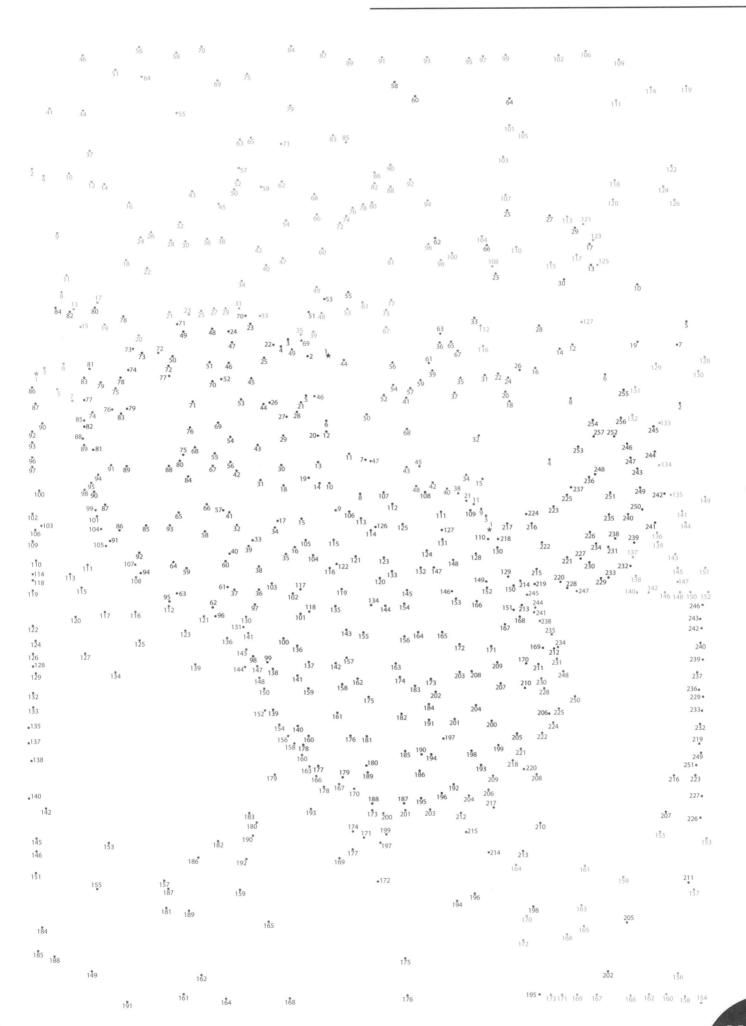

# Coral Reef

## ORDER OF COLOR SECTIONS

# Subterranean River

**ORDER OF COLOR SECTIONS**

sea blue 102
teal green 133
pale gray 36
light brown 262

mid brown 331
dark brown 126
black 100

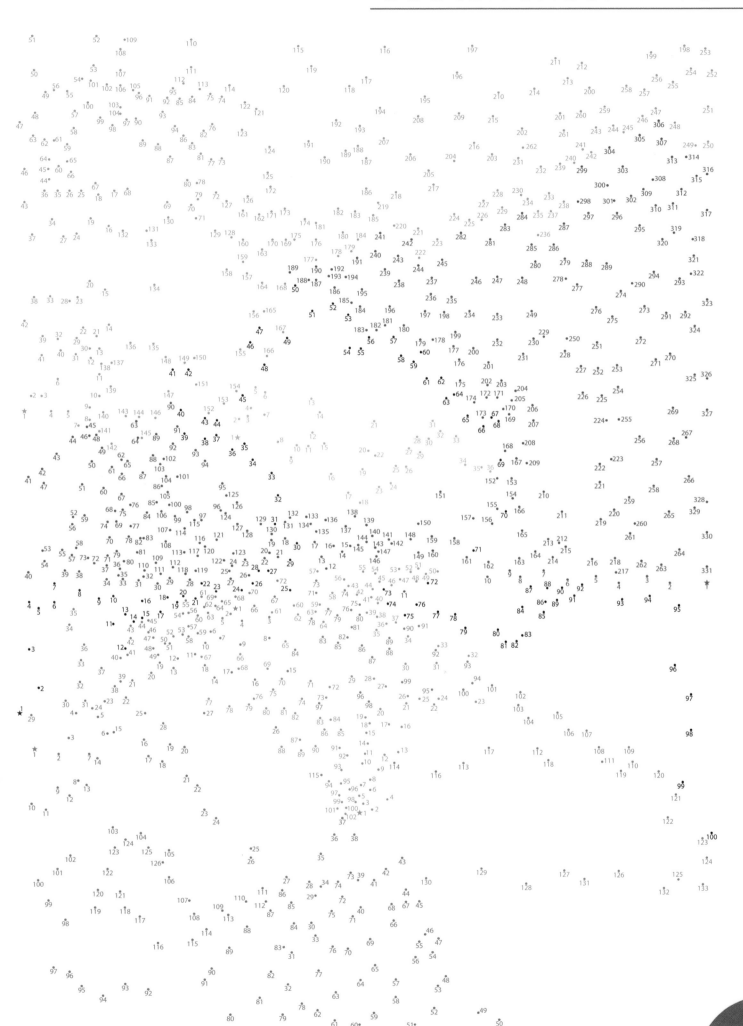

# Wildflowers

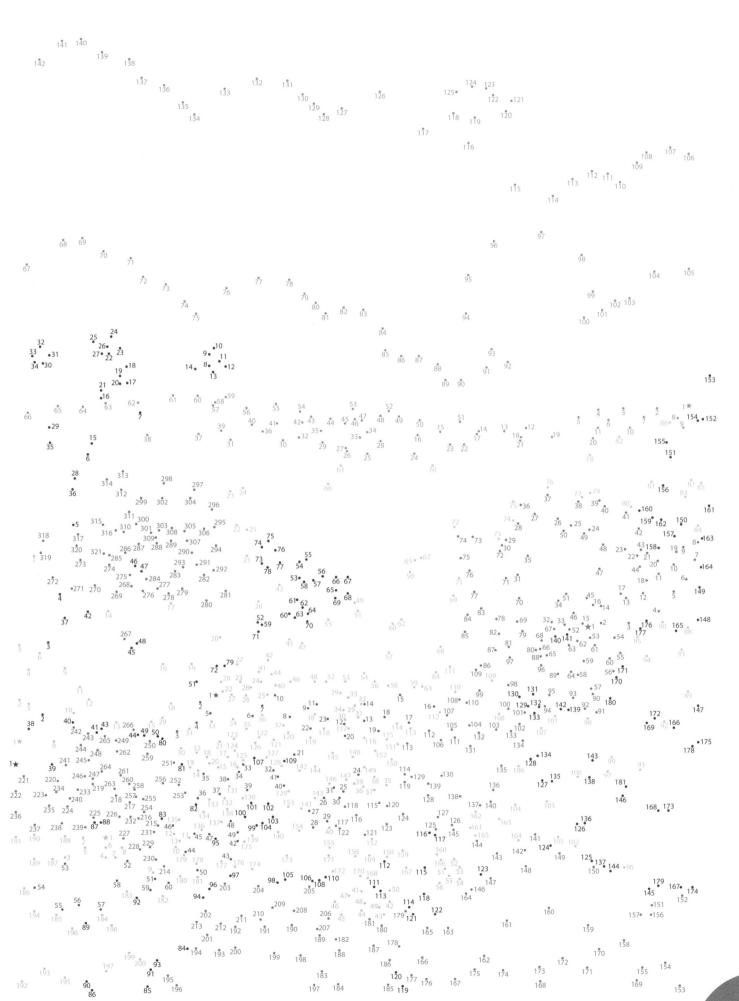

# Hallelujah Peaks

# Hallelujah Peaks

**ORDER OF COLOR SECTIONS**

pale gray 358        forest green 204
moss green 400       dark brown 119
light brown 154

# Tropical Bliss

## ORDER OF COLOR SECTIONS

bright blue 95
sand brown 77
leaf green 478
dark blue 79
dark brown 85

# Sunset at Sea

# Rushing Waterfall

**ORDER OF COLOR SECTIONS**

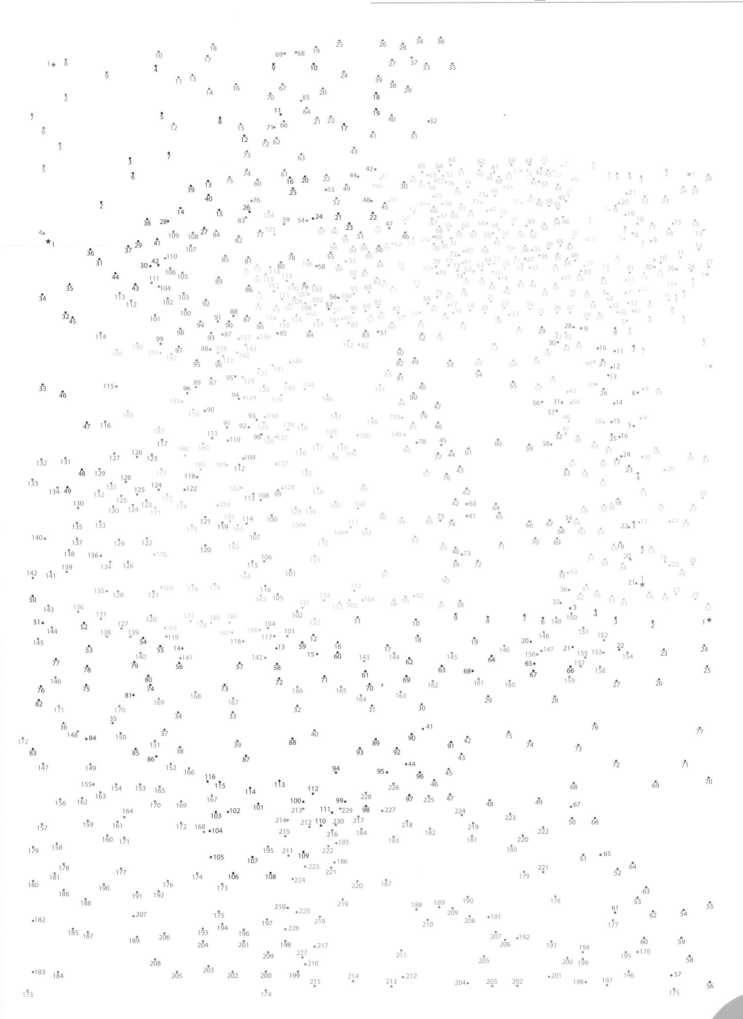

# Sunflowers

## ORDER OF COLOR SECTIONS

golden yellow 145
light orange 44
burnt orange 199
leaf green 207

brown
  back left flower 24;
  back right flower 26;
  large flower 80

# Alpine Mountains

## ORDER OF COLOR SECTIONS

lime green 65
orange 53
mid green 105
fuchsia pink 230

mountain peak purple 90
plum 107
forest green 270

# Tropical Flowers

# Marble Caves

# Falling Leaves

# Falling Leaves

# Prickly Customers

## ORDER OF COLOR SECTIONS

golden yellow 54
lime green 428
orange 114
leaf green 318
fuchsia pink 398
bright red 170
royal blue 159
dark green 102

# Cherry Blossom

# Lava Flow

## ORDER OF COLOUR SECTIONS

**golden yellow**
top section 68
lower section 52
**sea blue** 303
**red orange**
top section 193
lower section 74

**bright red** 126
**forest green** 94
**brown** 138

# Grand Canyon

## ORDER OF COLOR SECTIONS

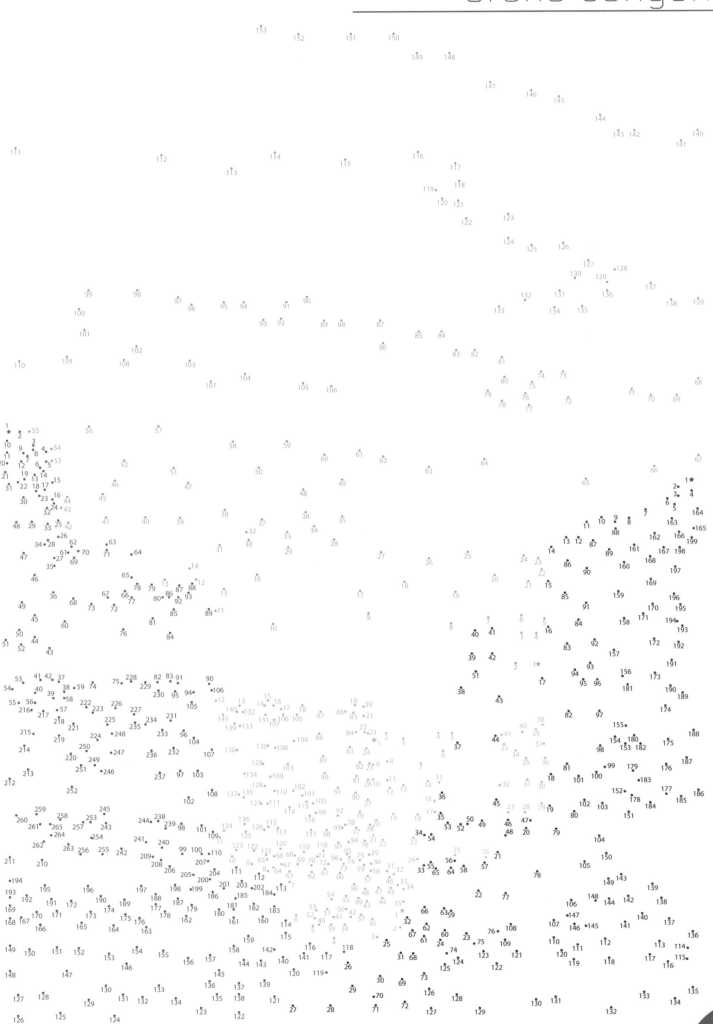

# Winter Berries

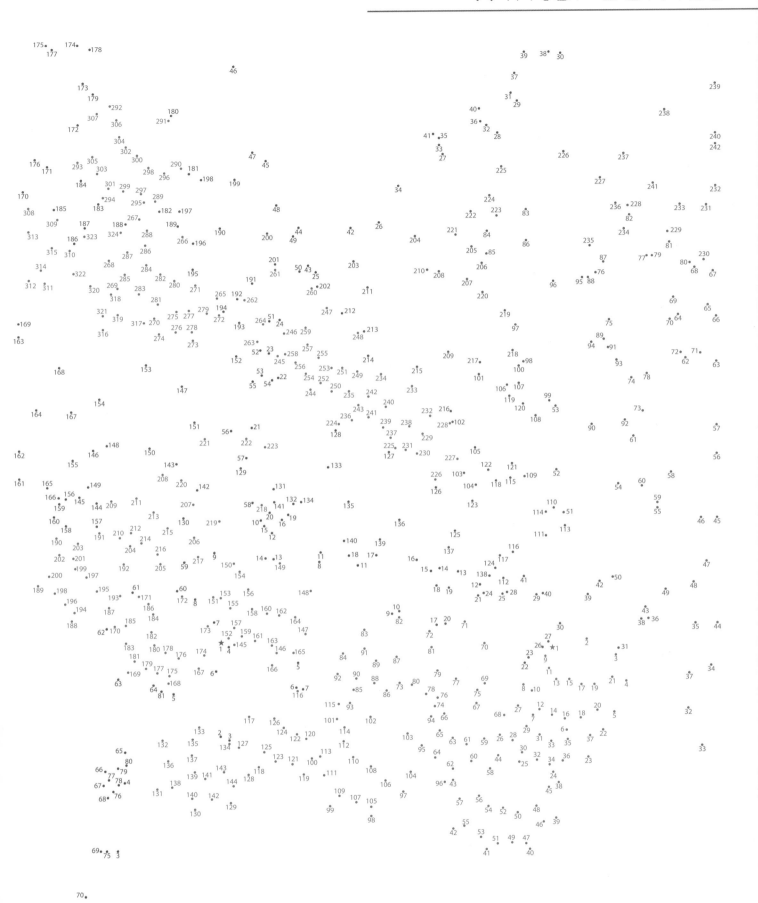

**ORDER OF COLOR SECTIONS**

forest green 242
berry red 324
dark brown 81

# Northern Lights

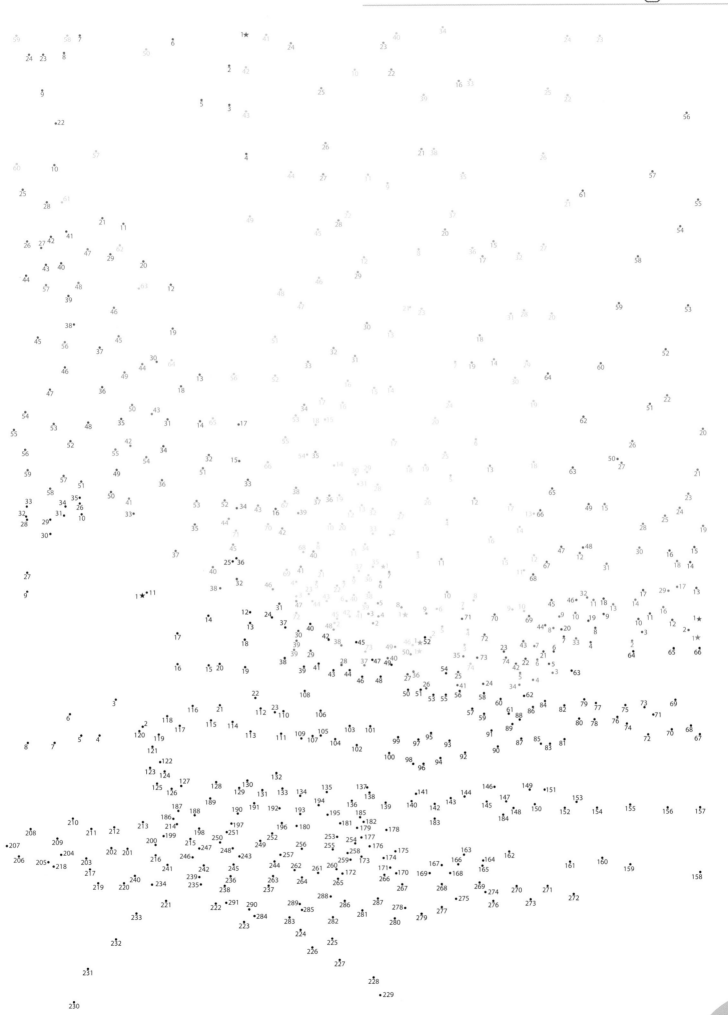

# Dandelion Time

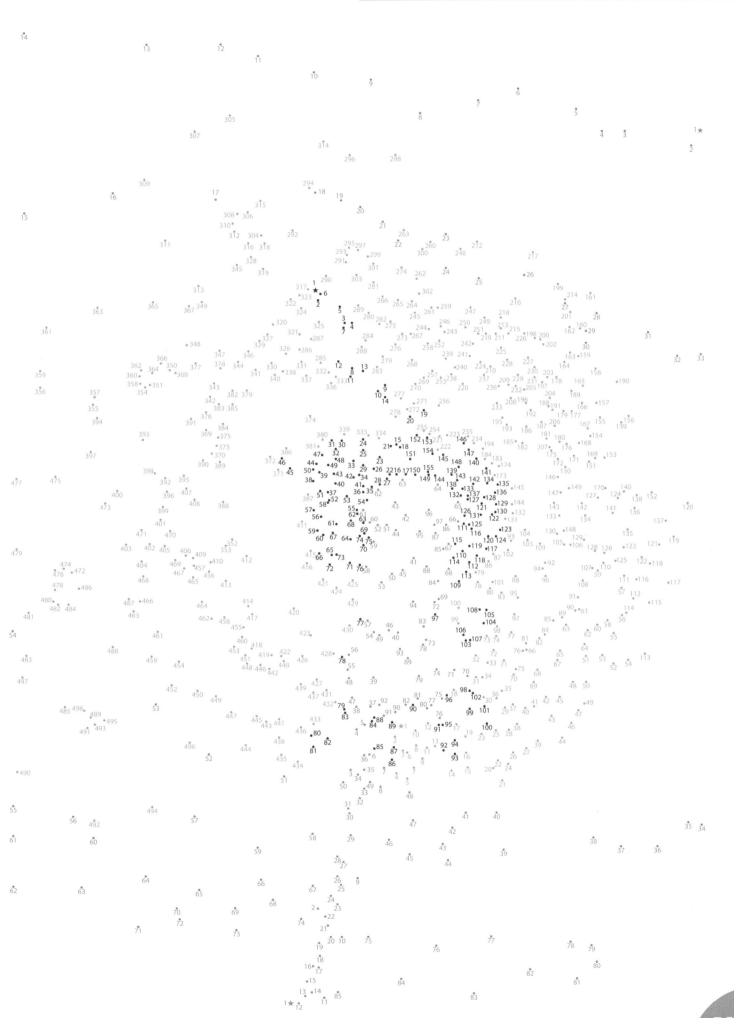

# Tuscan Vineyard

## ORDER OF COLOR SECTIONS

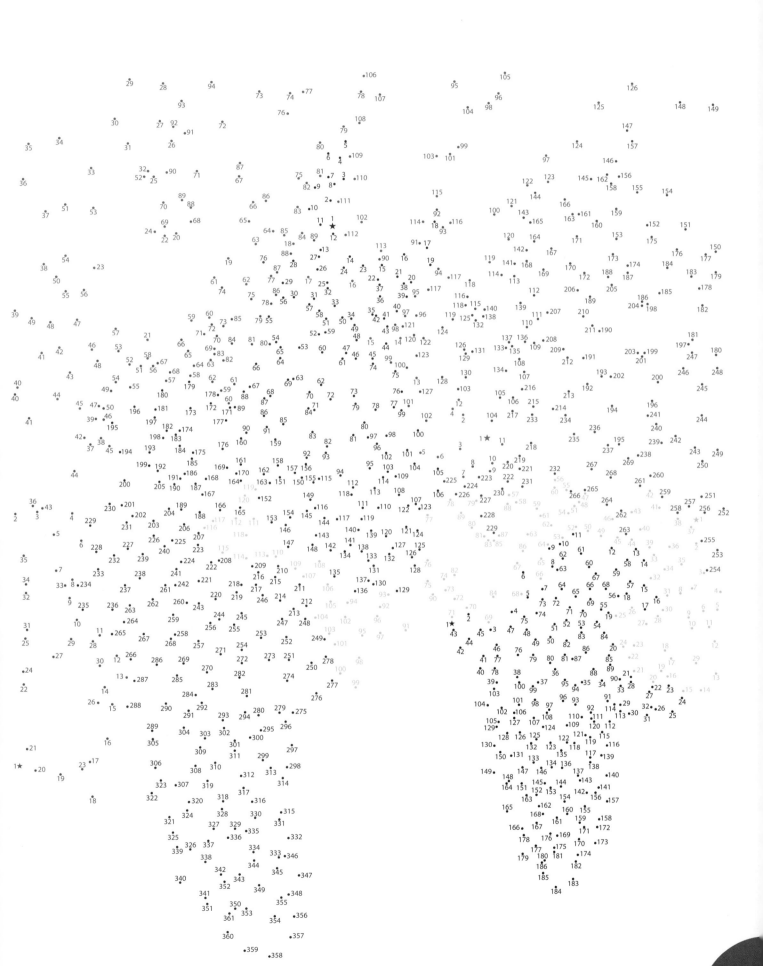

# Fruit Trees

**ORDER OF COLOR SECTIONS**

golden yellow 117
mid orange 133
reddish orange 145
forest green 223

# Bright Bouquet

## ORDER OF COLOR SECTIONS

# Toadstools

## ORDER OF COLOR SECTIONS

grass green 133    burgundy red 112
bright blue 39    brown 124
bright red 217    forest green 217

# Wild Roses

# Wild Roses

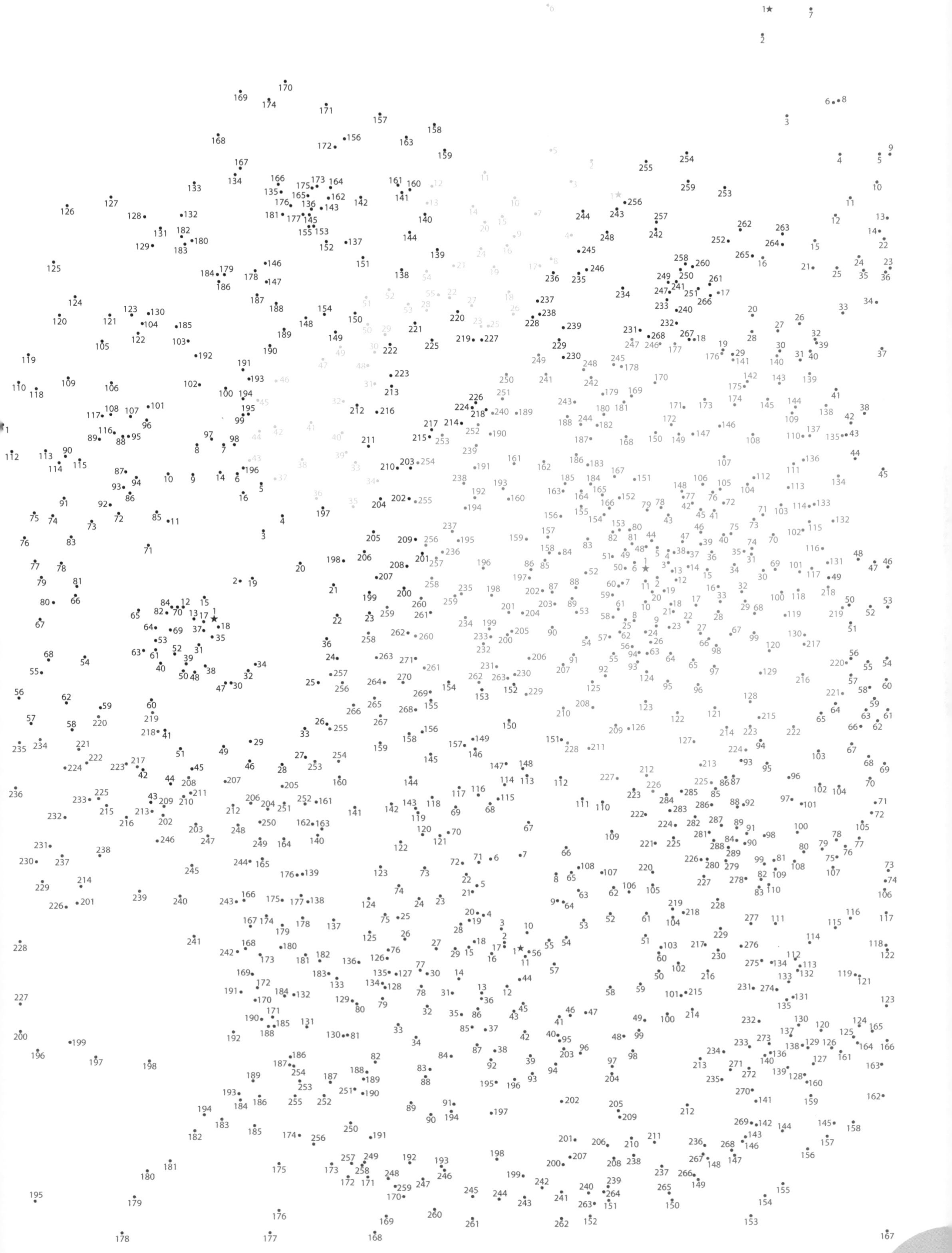

# Norway's Fjords

# Rio de Janeiro

## ORDER OF COLOR SECTIONS

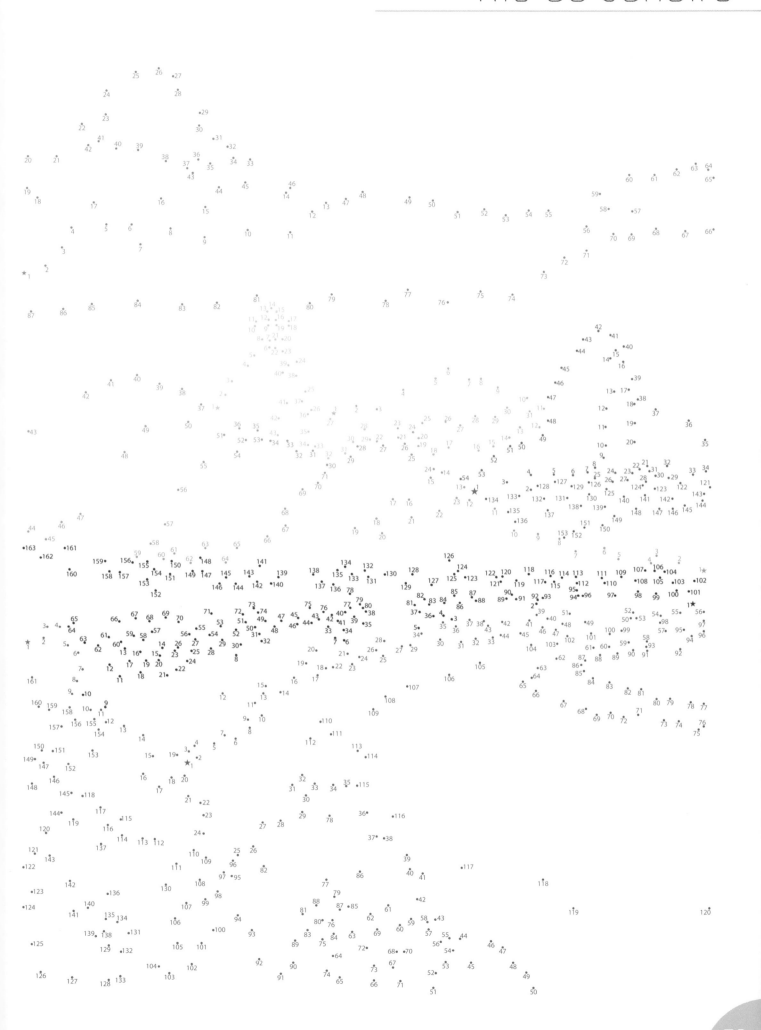

# Tulip Fields

**ORDER OF COLOR SECTIONS**

# Dot-to-Dot Index

Use the thumbnail images on the following pages to select the design you want to tackle next, or to help if you need any guidance when completing the puzzle.

**Down in the Jungle**
Page 17

**Fields of Gold: Corn**
Page 19

**Pine Cones**
Page 21

**Coral Reef**
Page 23

**Subterranean River**
Page 25

**Wildflowers**
Page 27

**Hallelujah Peaks**
Page 29

**Tropical Bliss**
Page 31

**Sunset at Sea**
Page 33

**Rushing Waterfall**
Page 35

**Sunflowers**
Page 37

**Alpine Mountains**
Page 39

**Tropical Flowers**
Page 41

**Marble Caves**
Page 43

**Falling Leaves**
Page 45

**Prickly Customers**
Page 47

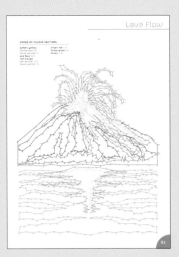

**Cherry Blossom**
Page 49

**Lava Flow**
Page 51

**Grand Canyon**
Page 53

**Winter Berries**
Page 55

**Northern Lights**
Page 57

**Dandelion Time**
Page 59

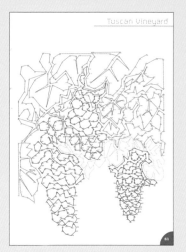
**Tuscan Vineyard**
Page 61

**Fruit Trees**
Page 63

**Bright Bouquet**
Page 65

**Toadstools**
Page 67

**Wild Roses**
Page 69

**Norway's Fjords**
Page 71

**Rio de Janeiro**
Page 73

**Tulip Fields**
Page 75

# Acknowledgments

**Quantum Books would like to thank the following for supplying images for inclusion in this book:**

**Shutterstock.com**
Vichy Deal, page 9
Sonya illustration, page 13 (top left)
Pictures_for_You, page 13 (top center and right)
NattapolStudiO, page 13 (lower right)

**Thanks to the following for their help in making this book:**

To our fantastic illustrator Shane Madden, thank you for bringing this concept to life and producing such wonderful artwork. It has been great fun creating this riot of color with you.

To Emma Frith Suttey for her expert checking of all the puzzles and constant enthusiasm for the project.

Thanks also to Tilly Davis, Charlotte Frost, Emma Harverson, Nicky Hill, Tokiko Morishima, and Julia Shone for their editorial work; and to Mike Lebihan for the design work and cover design.